DROPS OF THIS STORY

SUHEIR HAMMAD

DROPS
OF
THIS
STORY

HARLEM RIVER PRESS

NEW YORK & LONDON

Published for **Harlem River Press** by:
Writers and Readers Publishing, Inc.
P. O. Box 461, Village Station
New York, NY 10014

Writers and Readers Limited
c/o Airlift Book Company
8, The Arenea
Mollison Avenue
Enfield EN37NJ

Editor: Patricia A. Allen
Book Design: Clive Giboire
Tenth Avenue Editions, Inc.
Assistant Designer: Suzanne Cobban
Cover Design: Terrie Dunkelberger
Cover Photograph © 1996: Tarek Aylouch

ISBN: 0-86316-243-6

0 9 8 7 6 5 4 3 2

Manufactured in the United States of America

I GIVE THANKS
TO THE MOST HIGH
FOR BLESSING ME

This is for 18-year-old
Suheir Hammad
and her sisters

AUTHOR'S NOTE

I told her to chop it all off. I didn't want the weight of it bending my neck no more. Didn't want to recognize myself. The hair stylist fought me on it. She said it would be a sin to shear off all those thick curls. Did I know how many people would kill for my hair? Did I care? She cut it off. All of it.

I wasn't going back. I wanted to live, to write. Cutting my hair was an extra measure to make sure I wouldn't lose whatever nerve I had left in me. I wanted to revolutionize. There was so much to do, to read, to experience, to write.

Two years had passed since I had even picked up *Drops*. I had put it away. Pushed it aside. Now, almost four years since I first started writing it, I wish I had looked at it more often—'cause it still sings true.

Stories are songs, and singers are prophets. No matter what we think of someone's politics or personal business, if they do us right with their song, "kill us softly," we listen, intent, to find ourselves in their voices.

I can't sing for shit, but I had all these stories demanding to be sung. I write, so I wrote them. *Drops* was written in the statistics class I failed. Jotted down on the bus, and I always missed my stop. I wrote it in the middle of the night, 'cause I was wide awake and tired of crying. Exhausted from it.

Once, in an Indian restaurant, a waiter asked me what I did. When I responded that I was a writer, he asked what I wrote about. Not knowing how to break it down, I answered, "I write about myself." "That's pretty boring," was his response.

These stories are one. Our story. We who believed graffiti was art. We knew our vernacular to be language as sophisticated and romantic as any other. We were fly and knew it, Brooklyn style. We fought and killed each other. Had babies and got beat up. We were never allowed outside, always under lock down. We ate pernil and stuffed grape leaves. Danced salsa and recited Quran for the dead. We worshipped Orisha by the church choir.

It was hard for me to go through the passages of *Drops*. Writing it, there was only a faint hint in the back of my mind that you would one day be reading it. Know I'm not the only one to sing these songs, this story. Know there's a lot not in here. A lot of stuff a younger me still couldn't write.

But this is it. I'm beginning to do what I'm supposed to be doing. What I was born to do. Sacrifices have been made and a lot of pain carried around. I asked myself: Do I need to write to live? I answered yes with every cell of my being.

I didn't get here alone. My family's gifts of spirit have strengthened me for this journey. My ancestors watch over and protect me. Orisha guide me. God blesses me.

I'm growing my hair back. After a year and a half, I miss it. Your roots never change. I know no matter what I look like, I'm still Suheir. Still my parents' daughter, child of God, Palestinian, descendant of Africans, woman. After all this time, I'm still writing. So that our stories be told. For revolution. For sanity. So that we don't forget. So we always remember. I is we.

Suheir Hammad

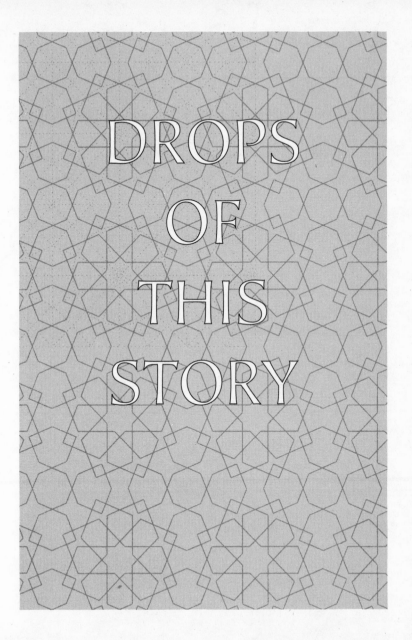

DROPS

OF

THIS

STORY

THERE'S this story that comes down to me all the time, wet. It don't come down like some big old rain storm, with thunder and lightning, that drives cars off the road in the middle of autumn nights. It ain't one of them pleasant summer showers either, them that can clear city streets in the middle of a hot working day. The kind of wet I'm talking about is the annoying, frustrating wet that barely manages to layer the concrete, yet somehow frizzes my hair into one big bush. The kind of teasing wet that seems to serve no other purpose than to let you know it's there. You know the type. It makes you look stupid to hold an umbrella and has people arguing over whether or not it's really raining.

This story teases my head just like that, 'cause I know I can't stick out my tongue to taste a rainbow or put out a bucket to catch flying sun beams. Loves to let me know it's there, taunting me, 'cause I'm the only one who can see it, hear it, smell it. This story laughs at me when I pull out an umbrella to shield my hair and then pinches my face just to let me know it's still around. What's worse about this kind of wet is that every drop hitting the back of my neck has it's own tale to tell.

SOMETIMES there's just a flood of little drops, those that amicably join together to annoy into submission. Those drops are stirred into the poetry that controls the breathing of my lungs. Those stories are the ones that make it into poems. There are plenty of them: the one that whispered the beauty of womanhood into my ear, the one that reclaimed my right to write with blades of grass on hot sun rays, the one that worshiped my prayers at the temple of Abraham. I save those little drops in an old Visine bottle under my pillow. I squeeze out a few tears whenever the breathing of my lungs becomes tired.

Colorful drops slip into my ear and travel down to my heart, where they wreck havoc on my system. I tell you that I've never been addicted to any type of drug. Ever. I never had to be. I'm addicted to music. I get high off a beat. Any kind of beat. Them drops hum Sam Cooke to me, while a Public Enemy riff beats the background of my brain. They order me to write about Abdel-Halem Hafez, and how I finally learned my parents' language when I was seventeen, just so I could understand his songs. I fell in love with his songs, and translations ain't no good. English is deficient in the language of love, translations ain't no good.

Them drops sing me into writing about Bob Marley's love of life and my love of his poetic music. They come down to the rhythm of a good merengue beat and slide down my body to the pulsing of a heated tabla drum. I need to write of how the tabla moves my hips to dance without my knowing it. How the tabla sounds like the voice of God on a good day. Them drops form my sweat after I've danced the pain away. They slide off my moving body until I'm left with a floor that needs to be mopped up with the pages of a book.

 THERE'S this one drop that burst to life on top my right eyebrow one day. This one wants me to write about my father. The wetness traveled down my face as though I had cried it out my eyes, as though it hadn't fallen from the sky. This is when I tell you about my father's heart of gold and mouth of bile. How my orphaned father— landless, motherless, nationless— can't deal with New York and can't deal with me. The only thing he can deal with is his bottle, and that relationship he cherishes. As though it were Hennesey, and not me, that had come from his loins. My father loves me, I know that now. I also know that he's killing me with his loneliness, his power, his liquor, his hate, and his love. My orphaned father can't deal with my attitude, my strength, my loneliness, my poetry, my love. He can't deal with me 'cause I'm just like him. He gave me all of the things that he can't deal with within himself. I'm just like him, only I don't drink. I write, and I cry. I work on only writing.

DROPS. They keep falling on, and I don't have an umbrella to shield me from the wetness. Most have a smell to them, and, through hypnotic gases, I tell you I was raised around the delicious stinks of the ghetto. Fried plantains and smoked reefers, my mother's stuffed eggplant and the neighbor's pork ribs. Our apartment building was always swaying with the smells of the East, the Caribbean, and the South. Them drops soak me till I let you know that the memories of my childhood stink deliciously of fried foods, spoiled fruits, and garbage that was picked up once a week, if the gods of sanitation were in the mood.

The smell of fish . . . and that time I saw a fish in the sink. I was about ten. My father was cleaning it up to fry, and he simply had it laying there. I thought fish came in them ready-made fillets. Screamed when I saw the creature. Huge, with it's head still on, it's cold fish eyes staring up at me. I screamed a loud-ass scream, and before I could get another breath of life's air into my lungs, my father's hand slapped down my mouth. I knew never to scream from fear in his presence again. My father hates the sound of fear, of female screaming.

Age 18 - My aunt's roof in Jordan, where my cousins + I would chill w/some falafel.

THERE'S the wetness that pours onto my paper out my pen, and I have to hang it to dry. Reggae beats dread the paper into long thin strands that I fashion into an umbrella, but it don't shield me from the wet. A saxophone's cry is carried in the drops and upon contact with my tired skin, the air is filled with the liquid words of jazzy poetry.

 SOME drops come feeling of fur. I write of the cats I had as a child. Them poor cats I used to be so afraid to hold that they always ended up in awkward positions in my embrace. My mother always said: Don't play too rough. They'll scratch up your face. A woman ain't much without it. It wasn't like them poor cats were going to attack me. I know that now. But I was afraid of loving them. Afraid of getting cut up.

THEM drops feel pretty good, but I soon feel others. These crawl down into my bra. Demand I sing the song about unwanted attention from men who really appreciated the body of a skinny five -year-old girl. Hard to tell, 'cause I know I can't make none of it up. I know I gotta tell it like I know it. There ain't no fiction here. Demands to be told, 'cause it's been shoved down too many throats. I feel it, taste it, even after the wetness has dried between my breasts. This one needs to be told poetically and carefully, so you don't blame me, and I don't blame myself. I brush this drop away for now. No fiction here. I can't yet write it poetically.

 RESTLESS wetness that annoys you into submitting to the will of the word. You know the type. Feels like a broken sprinkler trying to drown the sad grass of a sad park filled with drug tools and other tools of sadness. Don't let you know it's coming, soaks you out of nowhere, and then your perfectly dry. The type of musky dampness that you hate 'cause you know you're not in the right place or with the right person to ease it into memory.

It comes in little beads that sometimes cut through the skin, to enter your blood stream and lungs as you breathe in life's air. One of them got me on the back of my left knee one day as I was jumping rope. This one, too, had it's own story to tell. The story of frustrated teenage boys. Teenage boys with bad skin and worse attitudes. Teenage boys who had to make me feel like I really was too ugly, too skinny to get any better. That story has the ending already written out, 'cause when I see them boys now it's all about, "Whassup baby? You don't remember me? We used to be so close." The only close I remember was their nasty breath telling me I was lucky to be with them, and I couldn't tell their girlfriends. That's what I remember.

 THE WETNESS sometimes storms my head in the guise of meteor showers, and the heat of it burns my soul until I realize that this story must be told. When my skin is suffering from the heat, words spurt from my spirit in drops of sweat, and I write of longing for a land I have yet to feel under my feet. This tale is part of them all, and it never whispers it's urgency; it shouts it in song. The call to and from Palestine and her love, that is the command that automatically straightens my back and refuses anymore of my tears. But this story needs to be told right. It'll be told by my anger and love. I have to tell it in such a way that I can let you, make you, force you to feel the loss of a land you have never felt

age 18 - all dressed up for a wedding

under your feet. I sometimes wonder if I'm up to the task of telling it the way in needs to be told. I wonder if I'll live long enough to write the million or so pages needed to explain this love of land. Other times I know I can and will make you, force you to understand what I'm talking about. All in one word. That word has yet to wet these pages and soak this soul, so I'll keep writing until I no longer need to.

Just as some drops of wetness are hot and burn, there are them that are cold and freeze. Them are the ones that speak the story of Brooklyn, the land that I've lovingly caressed under my feet. My sneakered feet. That story will be told by my walk. My sneakers will tell of all the stray dogs I had to kick out my way home from the bodega on the corner. The crack vials I had to jump over, and the empty forty ounces that rolled under my steps. The streets of Brooklyn and how my Fayva sneakers were worn out every couple of months from the concrete, that story. How I used to search that same concrete to find a lone rusty dime with which to buy some Lemonheads or Cherry Bombs. Them are the stories my wet feet will tell.

MY HAIR hangs low with the dampness of the wet that comes from nowhere, and another story is told. About how I was taught that a girl's beauty lies in her hair and her virtue; be a virgin with long hair. That was all and good for some ivory princess in some ivory tower, but my hair had to be braided into submission 'cause it was too thick, too curly and basically too wild to let loose. Anyway, loose hair meant a loose woman, that's what my father said. My mother must have believed him, 'cause she always wore her long hair in a tight bun that gave her serious headaches. My braids were toys for the kids standing on the lunch line behind me. Twirling them, pulling them, feigning double dutch with them. My father forbade me to cut my hair, as though it were growing on his head. It made him proud, and it broke my mother's back as she would comb through the tangles. It made my father proud to have a daughter with such long hair; be a virgin with long hair.

There's a wetness that tells of the butcher room where I worked in my teenage years every Saturday in the back of my father's store in Queens. Weekend mornings spent wrapping chopped meat and quartered legs while listening to the classics on the radio. Depending on the holiday season, I would be pricing chitlins to Barry White or weighing turkeys while bumping to the Temptations. The neighborhood was filled with Southerners who taught me the magic of collard greens and sweet potato pie. Reminds me of what a sight I was in my bloody white butcher's coat and awkward growing spurts. Tells of picking up sides of beef that had been placed on saw dust covered floors and wrapping flank steaks after removing the fat with a plastic ice scraper. I don't eat much red meat no more.

MY SKIN tried to become resistant to these drops, this story, and the ensuing sleepless nights littered with writing, typing, and dryly crying. Unfortunately, my leather seems only to absorb all the moisture and has me writing, typing, and dryly crying through the day. What good does this tired skin do me if it can't stop the aggression of this story (in all of it's forms) from keeping me up at night?

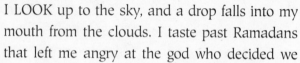

I LOOK up to the sky, and a drop falls into my mouth from the clouds. I taste past Ramadans that left me angry at the god who decided we needed to fast so our sins would be forgiven, and so we could empathize with the hungry. All I knew was that I was already too skinny anyway, without having to starve for the sins of the hungry. I hated explaining to the other kids every year how I couldn't eat the school lunch that day 'cause I was fasting. I would eat at sunset. I got sick of explaining fasting to grown teachers who should've known better. The worse part was when they would serve chicken patties in the cafeteria, and I'd have to watch all the other kids, whose appetites were already spoiled from too many Skittles and Charleston Chews, chew on my favorite food. What I'd eat at home later, my mother's food, which I knew took hours to prepare, was never as appreciated as that nasty patty would have been.

My fingers sometimes mold the wetness into a toy that I keep nearby as I write this story out. Didn't have many toys when we were growing up. My parents needed money to spend on five kids with big stomachs, not toys. I did have one Barbie though. I got her when I turned eleven, and damn, was I impressed with her! It bothered me only slightly that Barbie didn't look at all like me, that I'd never look like her, and that she actually had a boyfriend. I was happy with her, even though I had really wanted a Cabbage Patch

Kid. That was the year when they were selling for a good $100.00 a piece. Do you remember that Christmas? Ridiculous waiting lists, riots at toy stores, and delirious parents spending money on a yarn-head doll, when their children with big stomachs needed to be fed. Anyway, Barbie was good enough. Until . . . I realized that she'd need her limo, pool, mansion, and a new wardrobe for every gala party she hosted. That shit cost money. That's when I decapitated her. I mean, really, she didn't look like me. And she was allowed to have a boyfriend.

There are stories of childhood illnesses that condense on the tip of my pen, and the wetness dilutes the ink. My mother would take me to the public clinic, where everybody spoke Spanish and no one spoke English. I was of no use, 'cause the only Spanish I took time out to remember were the cuss words. The waiting room was always packed with people scurrying around like roaches dizzy from Raid. My mother would try to get this Pakistani doctor to check me out, 'cause he was Muslim. She figured that even if he was too tired to be competent, after seeing all them kids, Allah would give him divine guidance, and I'd get better. I thought that Pakistan was Palestine, or at least close by, so I thought he was pretty cool. Until he stuck me with the inevitable needle. Then he wasn't so cool no more. If I didn't cry, I'd get cheese doodles to eat on the way home. So I shoved back boogers and tears while my mother signed the Medicaid papers.

STREAMS of wet travel down thighs. I write about my big butt fetish. My love of the booty. My mom has a big old butt, but no, she had to give me her cheekbones and the ability to give biting dirty looks instead. I, therefore, am stuck sweating the big butts of men on the basketball court. I guess it's some sort of twisted compensation fixation (if I can't have a big butt, I'll have someone who does). So, I've become a connoisseur of the bubbly (booty). My use of adjectives has expanded over the years to include: the perky good morning butt, the rice and beans butt, the I'd love to thank your mother butt, the baggy jeans fit tightly where it counts butt . . . . This is part of the story I think I'll keep to myself.

Little ticklers swim down my shirt to poke me in the ribs. Coax me into blushed embarrassment. The time I had to pee so bad, I pulled down my pants before I reached the bathroom. Realization hit afterwards that my entire, unforgiving family was in the kitchen. They all just happened to look my butt's way in time for the sore sight of my butt disappearing into that tiny bathroom. I can laugh now.

AT TIMES the drops drizzle down, hitting my windshield, forcing me off the road on hot autumn nights. As the wipers do their business, I jot down on an old, crusty napkin. Driving home from Queens every weekend after working all day in the meat room. In that forty-minute ride I was free. Free. My father was behind me, and I hadn't reached home yet. The system would be slamming out TKA and Al B Sure, KRS-1 and Bob Marley. The road was mine, and my car, all bright red and loud, was the me I was afraid to be. I wouldn't want to feel the presence of anything other than the road, the gas pedal, and the bass pumping into me. If guys tried to get my attention while I was in communion with the god of speed, I'd just press the gas some more until I drove to the milky way. Sun beams were the only things flying by my window.

 THIS annoying liquid caress has me up writing at odd hours of the day. It just won't quit. No . . . as a matter of fact it does quit, right when I need it not to, right when I can't breath without those drops filling my lungs. This story wants to be told. My mouth is filled with the spit of it, and I gargle to let myself know I need air. Sucks up my air and spits it out.

The ocean below my knees. I write about that creepy white guy on the bus going home from school. That white guy with the fish eyes. His eyes were dead and glassy, like the fish in the sink, and pointed towards me through the too, too long bus ride. He was staring at my body as though I didn't have on that bulky jacket, those baggy jeans, and my brother's huge sweater. His eyes made me feel naked. As though I were sitting on the bus buck naked. Naked and swimming in an ocean full of woman-eating sharks. This white guy, with the glassy dead stare, saw my discomfort and got off on it. I wanted to demand my token back, I hadn't paid for this. I wanted to shove him out the window. Pull out his eyes. But I was too tired, and it was raining. It was raining, and I was too tired to let this creep get me soaked in the rain. When I got to my stop, I felt his eyes follow me off the bus, into the pouring rain, down the block, and into the shower to wash away his fish stare. The rain had soaked me anyway.

My 8th grade graduation.
First time I blow dried my hair.

BEADS form on my forehead, and I sing the song about the neighborhood women who usually had little beads of curl sheen or gel easing down their foreheads, escaping the rollers beneath their kerchiefs. If it was Sunday, they were dressed in pastel or white, with their 12-karat rings encasing every finger on the hands. Sundays were boring. The weekdays had the mothers on street corners calling this José or that Julio to get his sorry self home. The mothers always took time to coordinate their outfits . . . in a Sunset Park Brooklyn kind of way. The leather pink pumps matched the shoulder-length earrings. The fluorescent green t-shirt complimented the yellow tube socks. Electric blue bubble-gum stretch jeans matched the head band, and the requisite name plate went with everything.

I feel the beads travel down my fingers, and I remember the feel of the sheepskin that only the really cool kids sported. If you were really, really cool, you got one of the dyed ones (either in money green or Mercedes blue). The sheepskins went along with, first, the Pumas and, then, the Addidas that were the status symbol of the hood. This was before the Gucci and Fendi mania that had little girls dating drug dealers so they could sport the new stuff before it came out on the streets. This was the time when a kid in a new Addidas suit received the respect of a diplomat as he was walking that limp kind of walk down the street. The wet of this story stains the sheepskin and makes the sneakers stink like they were caught out in the rain after a hard game of ball.

Emerging from the cracks in the sneaker-pounded concrete. How I was always too small to play handball. It's not like you need to be a giant to play the game, but it was always the taller kids who were picked first, and I'd have to wait until someone got tired or had to go home 'cause their mama was hanging out the window yelling their name. Maybe there's another reason I wasn't picked too much. I wasn't that good at it anyway. Most of the time the girls didn't play. We just watched the guys play.

 AS I SIT in a steaming ginger bath, it slips into the tub with me. I try to scrape it off the tiles, the shower curtain and my skin, but it's clinging to me, becoming a part of me. Using the loofah my parents bought from some Arab store on Atlantic Ave., I scrub. So hard that I begin to bleed, and before I realize it, the wetness has entered my lungs through my blood stream.

Trickling continually onto my head on one particular spot, like some old method of torture. The soft spot on my head allows the drops to enter my skull. My brain waves swim in this story.

w/ Dad, 7th grade science fair.
I won 2nd place.

MY EARS are filled with the natal juice of this tale. I remember the time before birth, and how I was chilling in my mother's belly. What peace a baby feels when all she hears is the voice of God telling her not to worry, she would be protected by spirits and jinns who watch her back. God whispers the names of her ancestors so that she would know to call them when she needs help. The time before birth, when she was just chilling. Before I knew how to write, this story was around, waiting to let me know it was there.

The special wetness found in the smell of a baby's neck reveals that there was something to be written before there was sheepskin, before there was liquor, fish eyes, salsa, before there was me. The moistness found in that special part of a baby's neck writes about divine innocence that flew away like a meteor once the first breath of life's air filled the lungs. It tells of how the residue of this divine innocence was not enough to protect the baby from the world around her. The residue taunted and teased her, letting her know it used to be there. She forgot the names of those ancestors who were supposed to be watching out for her. They must have forgotten her name too, 'cause they sure wasn't looking for her. They wasn't watching out for her.

THE SALT of this humid speaks of the fist time I changed Omar's diapers. Tastes of his baby whimpering as he waited for me to change him. He was just lying there, waiting patiently for my nine -year-old self to get to it. Looking like a devious little man who was up to no good, he directed his four-month-old brown eyes on me and watched my face intently as I opened his diaper. I realized that it wasn't soiled and just looked at him, wondering why he'd been so cranky. As our eyes met, he let out the cutest baby gurgle, and a stream of warm baby pee that traveled right into my gaping mouth. I couldn't move. I was just standing there while he worked that upstream river to get me in the eye, in the nose, and then back to my mouth. Once again, my entire unforgiving family was there just in time to catch me swallowing in shock. It was just baby pee, it didn't really have a taste. Like funny water, that's all. Little drops fell off my nose and tickled his belly. I can still hear his baby laugh.

The sweet smell of this wet, and a story, on Sabrine's smile. My sister Sabrine, who just may be the sweetest person on Earth. Maybe too sweet. I was horrible to her when we were growing up. There was so much hurt and fear in our home, it was obvious the nicest one would get the brunt of it. It wasn't like Sabrine deserved it. Tried to please everyone, but no one in that family could ever be pleased as long as we were living the way we were. After my father would yell and beat on me, I'd go pick a fight with Sabrine or, even meaner, ignore her. I know she didn't deserve it. I want to tell her story so she could forgive me. The thing about Sabrine is, she's already forgiven me, and I don't know if I deserve it yet.

I can feel the congealed liquid flow from my hands as I write about the time my brother Sameeh busted his head open. We were jumping up and down on my parents' bed, and he fell off and hit the radiator with his big baby head. He was about two at the time, and my parents' only son out of four children. My parents rushed him to Coney Island Hospital in our first car, a used station wagon that my father had saved up for and finally bought that week. The car was stolen while my parents were inside the hospital, getting Sameeh's head stitched up. I cried over my brother's head and my father's car. I was reminded that my siblings all follow my lead, and why couldn't I just sit down like good girls do? Why was I jumping on my parents' bed? Why did I let the baby bust his head? Never mind that I was six and wasn't allowed to play outside, so I had to amuse myself inside a three-room apartment.

The moistness belies the secret of my sister Suzan's tears as she cried with me as I talked of leaving my father's house. I told her I just couldn't take it anymore. I was dying. Suzan, who doesn't cry at weddings, funerals, beatings, or good-byes, cried her soul out with me. Our tears mixed together, and she hugged me tighter than I had ever been hugged and let me know she would always love me. Throughout her entire sixteen years, Suzan had never told me she loved me. I have to write the story of this woman who was born cool, she doesn't have to worry about it. This woman who loves the New York Yankees. This woman who doesn't like to dance but loves music. Suzan, who looks out for me as though she were my older sister and not the other way around. Suzan, who I worry about, 'cause sometimes I think she's just too strong. Sometimes I can feel how tired she is. Knows when I'm working on a poem, even when I don't tell her.

 THIS STORY keeps me up at night. If only it were a simpler tale. If I could write of summers at the Cape and winters spent skiing, it might be easier. If it were more uniform, more constant, it would be easier to write it, to tell it, to live it. I don't think anything will ever come easy for me. Nothing has so far, but so what?

THE WETNESS flows through these fingers. I write how I've never held a man's hand while I was walking with him down the street. Once, when it was really cold, I put my hand inside this guy's jacket pocket, and he warmed it for me. That was nice. But even then, I knew our hands didn't fit right together. I always see couples walking hand in hand down the street, and I can't understand it. You can tell that most of these people don't belong together, so why would they pretend they do? Who are they fooling? I don't understand holding hands, linking souls, sharing spirits, with someone you know you don't belong with. Not that hand holding is some kind of cosmic practice that leads to eternal marriage, but if you lie to yourself a little lie, you'll believe it until it turns into a big one.

There ain't no love story here. Never been in love. I'm sure I've seen love, but my eyes are so accustomed to ugliness, I'd probably mistake it for something else. There is no love story here. I can write of all the guys who swore up and down that they loved me. I would doubt them (still do), not because I don't believe I deserve love. I just didn't believe it could be so easy. If only I had a dollar for every brother who thought they could get rid of my nightmares by putting me to bed. I just don't believe it's that easy. Nothing good ever comes easy. If a man falls in love with me instantly, he'll fall out of it just as fast. There have been people that I cared a lot about, but I never let myself care too much.

THE DROPS of this story carry the names of all them kids I went to school with. Them who were taught drugs were bad, but readily available. If they weren't addicts, they were dealers, unless their parents beat them bad enough. Then they were more scared of Pops than peer pressure. I grew up in the wet heat of the crack epidemic. I saw some of my friends die a slow death of urban cancer, while the boys they used to hang with were sporting eight ball jackets and Nikes. Crack vials were planted in school yard gardens, and the poor reaped the harvest. Nissan Maximas became the drug dealer's calling card. Crackheads would go up to the window, with their stinking bodies, torn clothes and sick spirits, and beg for a little favor until their next check came in. Grandmothers became the mothers to babies born addicted. Grandmothers lost their sons and daughters to some new kind of demon. Lost their social security checks to their lost children. This wetness is made up of the tears of those grandmothers who didn't ask for nothing that came their way. Them grandmother tears.

The moistness interrupts my breathing and commands I write about all them child mothers. Little girls who popped children out of their bellies like biscuits. Immigrant parents who didn't expect their little girls to have sex before they were married. Single mothers who expected their kids to do better. Baby mothers would practice braiding their babies'

5 year old me
at Coney Island!

hair on Barbies; be a virgin with long hair. Little girls who believed the mouths of big boys who said that this was what love was all about. Some of them boys weren't so big, and none of them were big enough to be daddies. None of them girls were grown enough to be mommies. Every time someone else got pregnant, the classroom would be full of talk about who the father was, or how could she have gotten pregnant when her boyfriend was in jail? Classrooms full of little mommies and daddies.

 FORMED on hot sun rays and dripped down at the speed of light. They burn holes in my shirt, stories. This is the one about how I can't handle real heat. After living in Brooklyn for seven years, I visited relatives in Jordan for a summer. One morning, my cousins and I were sent to the bakery down the rocky hill to get fresh pita bread for breakfast. The Arabic word for bakery, *furon*, translates to "oven." It must have been at least a hundred degrees that day. As we were waiting in line in our pajamas (a girl raised in jeans and sneakers walking around in her pajamas), I had a heat stroke. It was real weird. All of these color spots swimming around my head, like meteors. This heat wasn't New York heat, it was dry and searing. By the time I came to, I had all of these people talking to me in Arabic. When I couldn't reply, they started to laugh. I was just another American tourist who couldn't handle the heat. I was an American to them, but to Americans I was just another immigrant; a waste of food stamps.

This story travels with me on the subway, the car, the plane. This wetness was with me in Jordan, wetting my cheeks, as I sat on a mountaintop where my uncle used to sit. Where he used to sit to get a good view of Palestine over the sea. This is the story I was born to write. The story of my uncle, *ami*, Hammad. At eighteen he was killed by Israeli soldiers, like too many other young men. Young men who preferred to die in the name of freedom than live a denied existence. This is the story I have to write, my uncle tells it to me in my dreams. He died in love. I, who have never been, write the story of this kid who died like too many others. I'll never know the girl that Hammad was in love with. Too bad. I wish she would help me write his part. Fill in the drops only a lover would know. Hammad is my spirit guide. I know that, 'cause he whispers it to me in my waking dreams. His name was one of those I forgot at birth, his death reminded me. The wetness down my cheeks reminded me of his part.

The drops sometimes join together to flood my head with memories of people I never knew. Young people who died needless, ugly deaths, like kids in the Brooklyn streets.

This story has too many names. Too many to remember them all. Palestinian kids massacred while dreaming. Young men detained for three-quarters of their lives only to be tortured to death. Palestinian girls who were raped and killed before they gave up names, or Palestine. This part of the story is made up of too many tears. It waters the anonymous graves of those kids who lived under occupation and died in the name of freedom. The drops of this story are carried on the wind to Brooklyn, where they douse me with strength.

 BEADS tickle my tongue, which I stick out to catch flying sun beams. They live in my mouth until they're ready to be told. Coy and teasing, kissing me as though we had been life-long lovers. Is my kiss. My wet kiss. Tickling my tongue until I let out a laugh through my pain, through my pen.

Sometimes swirls in the night, illuminating meteors. When I look out the window, I see a sight similar to Van Gogh's *Starry Night*. This writing has me going insane, in a Van Gogh way. I can't cut off my ear though, it's another canal for this story to travel. I hear it whisper to me over the typewriter's din. I hear it screaming at me as I study statistics (poorly). It just won't go away.

SOMETIMES, I get lost in a Frida Kahlo painting, the paint melts under my gaze and travels to the floor, where it covers my sneakered feet. I think sometimes stories would like to be painted, but my art lies through the pen. I can barely draw a straight line, much less live one. I can't draw, paint, sculpt or sketch; only with words do I work. I used to find it frustrating to see people create pure beauty out of anguish or pleasure, while I couldn't draw a straight line. I got over it. Some people feel the need to create beauty and wind up having kids instead. Most created by this greedy need come out ugly and mean. 'Cause they weren't conceived out of pure pleasure or divine anguish.

 I USED to tell my mother that maybe if she had waited before getting pregnant with me, she would have realized the mistake that was her marriage before she had four more kids. But now I think my mom knew before she even got engaged that this thing with my dad wasn't gonna be cool. My parents have the type of love that I hate. It's the type that I never want to wet my sheets with. Love that is forced out of years of hurt and fear. The type you feel when you fear being alone, 'cause what if you realize that after years of a bad marriage, that life sucks anyway? At least you're stuck with someone for the ride.

MY FATHER let me know I was going to get married. Our way, his way. Never mind that at eighteen, I didn't have a way. He tells me that there's a respectable young man who wants to come over and ask for my hand in marriage. This wetness tells of how this fool drank all the drinks my mother offered without thanking her once. Proceeded to burp after every swallow, you guessed it, without excusing his rude self. I should have known. I looked out the window and saw his balding head in the sunlight. He was wearing a pink shirt. A pink shirt. I don't get this arranged marriage business anyway, but the least this fool could've done was wear a suit. He had a belly, a big nasty belly. No butt. I didn't even look.

My mother kept nagging me to put on some makeup, telling me that I should feel complimented to have so many suitors. Like I wanted them. Then my father yelled at me for not wearing a dress. How was I supposed to explain that this was the twentieth century and people didn't do this in New York. In Palestine. Or in hell? I felt like a show horse. This story is lived out too often. Had me worried that I was gonna end up in a dry, unwanted union.

Beads were forming on the wide forehead of this would-be husband. He wasn't the only one either. They all wanted to marry me, and none of them ever talked to me. They went through my father. Never talked to me. They would see me at a wedding, where I'd be all done up, dressed fly and dancing my ass off. All they knew was that I was somewhat tall, said to be smart, drove my own car, and had already been poor, so I wouldn't expect too much. This is how people end up holding hands and linking souls even though they know they don't fit right. There was the guy who didn't say a word to me all night and called my dad the next day, talking about how he just had to have me. The one who had a crush on me for two years before his mother let him know I was too educated for him. The one who wanted to test me before making up his mind. The list drips on down the page. Drops on my page.

 THERE is the rain that pummels the D train's windows as it's going over the bridge. I hear it yelling at me from outside as I write about the shrunken Asian women sitting across from me. Each have plenty of shopping bags filled in Chinatown. Bags filled with the secrets of their memories. I can hear them talking and wish I knew what they were saying, so that I could write them into this story. Shouting at each other as though they were on different continents, but they sit completely still. This fascinates me, 'cause when my father yells, his eyes pop out, his veins bulge, and his hands go up. These women are telling their stories real cool, but through their eyes. I can tell the subject must be juicy. Maybe it's sex talk, or some hot gossip about a neighbor. They just may be talking about how I need to mind my business and go to sleep.

The crying baby on the train. His hungry tears make up part of this wetness. This breathing of my lungs. This baby cries out in the train, or in the middle of the night. This story spurts out of ancient radiators that parents have to put milk crates around so baby won't go near them. The baby's hands are always burned.

STEAM burns my hands, and I wonder how I can even hold a pen. But the decision is not mine, is it? If I were asleep, my hands would still be moving by the power of something other than my talent or will. The wet dries out anything that may distract me from its commands.

I don't know if I'm up to the telling of this tale. If it were easier, more constant. If I could be promised that every word would be understood. Every meaning appreciated. This wet holds no promises, only commands. I have to cry it out and hope it finds its way.

Probably end up lying dead on some beach, exhausted by the waves of writing this, whatever it is. Probably end up in some sewer alley, like Edgar Allen Poe. The Raven shakes the beads of moisture off her wings and down onto my paper. I hear the Raven calling me in the middle of the night. Hear a lot of things in the middle of the night, 'cause I'm wide awake.

 LIKE prayers from the lips of the faithful. This is the story of God. How God is within me, with me, apart of me. While writing it, I ask why I was chosen, fated to write it out. Wonder if I loved God a little more, would this rain let up a bit? I answer my own stupid question with another. How can somebody love God more or less? If you do, you do. You can't measure the degree or the amount. I can't increase the love I have, I can only nurture it. I was born with it already planted inside of me. This story wets the love of God and plants it in schoolyard gardens, where the poor reap the harvest.

Me + Cido -
my grampa

THE OPEN sewers of refugee camps carry this wetness to the streets of New York. The smell of urine, poverty, and frustration stink up the wetness of this story. Life in the refugee camps bully men out of little boys and little women out of tired girls. The camps aren't made up of tents anymore. Stone roof units hold the people down now. Pictures of too many dead freedom fighters are proudly displayed in every home, mosque, church, and store window. Drops form on the keys to some stolen home that was lost years ago. Them keys are hung right near the bed, as though, in the middle of the night, the family was gonna go back. As though grandparents were gonna return to Palestine tomorrow.

The stink counters the sweet smell of my grandfather's pipe. This is the my maternal grandfather, who, for forty years, refused to buy a home, 'cause he just knew he was gonna go home tomorrow. Whose wrinkled face was the color of deep brown tree bark. One decade, he got mad at my grandmother and built himself a room on the roof. He lived there with his pipe, his prayer rug, and his chickens. You could do that in Middle East. He would raise the birds with love and respect, and when it came time to kill them, he would recite a prayer for their souls and slit their throats. My grandpa would yell at me when I wouldn't eat his chickens. I was used to Perdue, not these sorry, straggly birds that just a few days ago I saw running around the roof. He'd give me one of his daughter's dirty looks and call me a spoiled American brat.

My father's wet breath orders me to write a story about my paternal grandfather. He died not even a month after the death of Hammad. Died of a broken heart over the murder of a son who had carried the family's name as his own. My grandfather prayed everyday, five times a day, for over sixty years (no one was sure how old he was). Never smoked. Liquid fire, which had addicted his sons, never once touched his faithful lips. This is the long tale of how my grandfather would walk an extra three miles out of his way so as not to pass the ladies who frequented the one European bar in his city, with their bare arms and legs. This drop of the story wonders what my grandfather's ghost thinks of me. I know that his son is with me. Hammad whispers his presence in the night, but I've never met my grandfather's spirit in my sleep. Maybe he loved God more than I do.

HOW can I pass my statistics class if I can't get this wet off of my brain? Count the names of the spirits who make up this story? It's teasing. Letting me know it's there. Taunting me with the promise of rest once it's done with me.

Driving through me like the D train on a track made slippery by wetness. I know now that this has nothing to do with me. Here before I was. This story will be told. I don't feel used though. The way some guys can make you feel, just tired. I just want to get it over with. Get it out. This train is going right through me. All I can do is stand there.

 DRIP of the bathroom faucet in our old Brooklyn apartment carried the wet of this story. Told the sadness of our only white neighbors. A grandmother, her two adult daughters, and two grandsons. Their all-American dream was acted out right next door. The eldest son became a drug addict and beat up on his pregnant girlfriend. The younger one, my age, began abusing his grandmother by the time we were in junior high. She came over one night to call the police on him. I let her in, even though she wasn't so nice to me. She'd always look at me through her wet, old woman eyes as though I was an alien or something.

THIS STORY flows to the beat of an Arabic dance song. I could write this entire epic with the sway of my hips. This story, with the shake of my hips. The sweat that forms between my breasts dries off and leaves the residue of innocence to taunt me. My shoulders sway to the sound of music and to the beat of the words. Nothing to do with me. I'm just a train it's riding to get to where it's going. I'm promised rest and sleep at the end of the journey.

 POETRY is my life's air. And the air humid with these words. Tell of Flatbush Ave and the assault of colors, smells, and sounds of the Caribbean in Brooklyn. Dancehall music oozes out of loud speakers like rivers. Men in crushed velvet suits of royal purple or money green, polish their pointy shoes while checking out the women on the street. The women being checked out are rolling their eyes and walking away snapping their gum. Africa is evident in the adornment of the bodies on Flatbush. Round here, however, the hair is adorned with orange and yellow extensions and glued on rhinestones, rather than cowry shells and *geles*. This time, cheap gold decorates black bodies, rather than prayer beads and sacred shells.

I write wet poetry. About Hammad and Sunset Park. On how Palestinians need to get over our internal colonialism. The British taught my mother to hate and to flatten her butt. Taught my father that he wasn't quite white, therefore not quite right. How we need to accept the Asian, the Mediterranean, the Crusader, and the African in us. Accept and deal with it.

 SHAME licks bodies. The story that keeps me from holding anyone's hand. I have nightmares of men staring at my little girl body and remarking on its beauty. I have memories of cousins playing a funny kind of horsey with me, even when I didn't want to. This story I've heard whispered in all languages, all accents. I knew as a child that everything was my fault. My doing. The drops enter my ear almost every time I hear a man remark on my alleged beauty. I can't feel beautiful in so much pain. I'll swear up and down that I'm not sentimental, but this story has me writing of how I want to hear, just once, that I'm pretty, and not feel dirty afterward. Not want to go home and wash the wetness away. The wet of ugly memories comes between me and my stuffed bunny at night.

WRAPS itself around my head. The first time I wrapped my hair in a *gele,* an African head wrap. Using material from Senegal, I shaped it around my head the way my friends had shown me. Wanted to wrap myself in the beauty of sisterhood. The ancestors remembered my name and whispered it to me under the material. I recalled past lives, when I had wrapped my hair everyday after washing it in the river. Washed my hair in ancient rivers that carried me in their flow.

I place drops of this story on my neck and wrists, on my temples and ankles, every morning, in the smell of coco-mango oil. A poet once asked me what a nice person smelled like. Replied coco-mango, and he smiled with the memory of the drops touching his skin. My mother hates the smell of my oil. My father doesn't notice it. He's not supposed to. Once, when I was experimenting with honeysuckle, he told me I smelled like a dead person. I rolled my eyes. He was serious. In Palestine, they placed honeysuckle on the pulse points of the dead body so that the spirit would smell good when it reached heaven. Anyway, who wants to smell like a dead person? I stick with coco-mango. The drops perfume me every morning.

Cowry shells that hang from my ears and adorn my neck once carried this wet. My sacred beads weren't blessed by a shaman, imam, or any man. They were blessed by me and

17 years old Nike fiend.
Couldn't tell me nothing!

my prayers. Rather than holy water in a bottle, I doused them with my sweat. Wore them when I danced to the sacred drum. I place them in my mouth when I'm hungry for love. Place them under my lashes as I cry. This story's wetness has blessed my beads, my cowries, and me. Bless me.

 SING the song of my mother's full day of labor pains. I was born on the 25th day of the 10th month of the year. Five o'clock in the morning, 5th day of the week. The number 5 is supposed to bring blessings and rid evil. I was born fat, a good 10 pounds. My legs clench just thinking about it. Good things don't come easy. My poor mother was in labor for a whole day. Her midwife was an Egyptian woman, and, delirious with pain, my mother told her that if we both lived through this birth, she'd name the baby after her. My mother says the woman was *samra*, like me. Samra means dark. My father says she was pretty. This wet afterbirth is the story of my name.

As this dew forms on the petals of morning flowers, it directs to my name. Suheir. Suheir means someone who likes to stay up late, female. *Lover of the night*. It's derived from an extinct flower that bloomed nocturnally and once fragranced eastern skies. The wind carries the oil of this flower to Brooklyn, to bathe me in its words. My father didn't tell me what my name meant until my first year in college. I wish he would have told me earlier.

I spent a childhood with too many girls named Maria, Tanisha, and Jill. Suheir sounded too much like *Sahara* or *Sue-her-hair* to make my life any easier. The kids were bad, but the teachers were worse. I would hate to get a substitute teacher, 'cause I'd have to go through the same thing all the time. Wait until I knew my name was next to be called, then shout out that I was present before I had to hear another tongue's rendition of my name. How did they read Suheir as *Sharar*? My resentment tells the story of how none of these teachers ever asked me how to pronounce my name, or what it meant, or where it came from. Or the way they read my last name as Mohammad even though it was Hammad. They did that to me at my eighth grade graduation, where I beat out all the ninth graders for a city writing award. The winner was *Shohar Mohammad*.

I love my name now. I love to say it, and to hear it said, correctly. Trying to make things easier for people, I used to answer to Sue. I don't anymore. Why should I? That wasn't the name born to me. How will the spirits know what to call me? I carry the essence of an extinct night flower. Cool. The drops prick my brain and let me know that this flower must have been a desert cactus.

TEARS out of my eyes. My bad eyes. The first time I was told I had bad eyesight, I cried all the way home. Sure my father would blame me for not being perfect. Even though my parents assured me it was okay, that it was even a sign of intelligence to wear glasses, I knew better. I had ruined my vision staying up late at night, reading. I would read by the light of the street lamp outside my window. When we got a night light, I'd sleep next to it, juicing it for its light. I could feel the wetness of my eyes dry out under the strain of squinting them all the time. I couldn't tell my parents that I had messed up my own eyes. I was sure it was my fault I was losing my sight. Sure that God was punishing me for wanting to know too much.

Wet my thirst for knowledge as I went through book after book. By the time I graduated elementary school, I'd read most of Shakespeare's works. My teacher would tell me that I should be reading Judy Blume or Archie comics, like the other kids. This is the same teacher who refused to call me Palestinian, 'cause, she said, it didn't exist as an ethnicity. When I said I had read Tolstoy in 7th grade, another teacher called me a liar in front of the whole class. Only after he grilled me on the story and the characters did he admit that maybe I had read the cliff notes. Those teachers wouldn't admit that a Black, Asian, Latino, or Arab kid could read the Western masters and understand them.

I read everything I could get my hands on. Before I knew of Alice Walker and Langston Hughes, I was reading the backs of cereal boxes. There was a time, before Naguib Mahfouz's words bought the wet to my eyes, when I would read the maxi pad box in the bathroom. This story, my story, has been with me for years and books. It watered the pages of all the books that formed my memory of words.

 IT LIVES on the back of my tongue. Where the taste of falafel and hummus mingles with the bite of plantain and curry. Pounded the garlic and peppers for my father's fava beans every Sunday morning. Why couldn't we just eat pancakes and bacon like everybody else? We had to have olives at every meal and pita bread with everything. I know now that I always loved that food. It's just hard to be different all the time.

I know now that this story was in the olive oil we sprinkled on our hummus. In the tomato juice that squirted as we prepared *taboulleh* for parties. When it became cool to eat hummus, falafel, taboulleh, and pita with everything, it was too late. I had already wasted years of trying to trade my *labeneh* sandwiches for peanut butter and jelly, which I didn't even like. I know now that I was just another immigrant kid, trying to fit in. But I never liked mayonnaise and cheese anyway. Never liked hot dogs and apple pie.

 THE DATES, pomegranates, figs, and cactus pears that my father brought home swam in the nectar of this story. I drank it. Chewed this song lives ago. I once swallowed a fig whole, and it planted this story in my belly. I've had a stomach ache ever since. Pomegranate juice once squirt in my weak eye, and the acid wetness mingled with my irritated tears. This story oozed out of the cactus pear I was peeling and entered my blood stream after it pricked my fingers. The nectar was swallowed by gods on some mountain top lives ago. The rain still carries the residue of the juice. Letting me know it's there.

I clean cucumbers and mint in the rivers that carry this story. Wash the mint for tea, and the cucumber for salad. My hands decorated with henna in the design of figs and mangos. Wash in the rivers that carry to the mouth of the earth. The center of the universe. God. Woman. The rivers carry the monthly blood of the earth, cleansing herbs and vegetables, flowing from my bloodstream. That which cleanses me.

THE SUN turns me a deep bronze in the summertime. My mother was always yelling at me to stay inside. I was *samra* enough. With my black hair, thick eyebrows, and little mustache, I looked foreign enough. Most people can never guess what language I speak, or which flag I kneel to. Old Latina women always thought that I was one of them new, newfangled Puerto Rican girls who didn't speak Spanish. Hindi women were always talking to me in their curry tongue, and when I'd let them know I wasn't Indian, they'd talk to me in Bengali. Anyway, I was supposed to stay out of the sun. I was dark enough.

The Arab movies my parents bought home were filled with blonde actresses whose eyes were the color of swimming pool water. It was in them eyes that this story was floating. I never understood why all the actresses were blonde when most of the people I knew were darker. I knew there was something wrong. Barbie. I saw the swimming eyes on the Latino stations, rap videos, and Hindi musicals. This wasn't just an Arab thing.

The story of self acceptance. Of finally not minding my skin, my hair, or even my mustache. Needs to be told. The drops whisper in too many languages, too many tongues. There are too many girls who think they're ugly, 'cause they can't swim in their own eyes. Want to look like Barbie. This is Barbie's obituary. Barbie was decapitated. She's dead.

19. Writing Class - my friend
is reading a draft in the corner.

HEAD filled with the brain fluid of this story. I can't sleep at night from the swimming of names behind my eyes. Pillow stained with drops that fell out my ear as I was lying down. The weight of a feather and the density of a rock. Weighing me down. Wonder if I'll fall to the bottom of this ocean of woman-eating sharks. Sharks who don't know my name. Ears are filled with the silent scream of this story. Weighing my head down.

 THERE'S no umbrella to shield my soul from the cold words dropping down on me like rocks. My memory conspires with this story to force me to write words that I'd rather not remember. Words that marked childhoods; nigga, spick, camel, bitch. Words used when people don't know your name. We all heard it, we all said it. We lived by it. Girls were bitches and sluts. Boys were niggas and faggots. Of course, there was the dash of motherfucker and bloodclot, along with the drop of *puta* and *pendeho*, to add to the stew. And man, we drank it down. We slurped up that stew as though it were nourishment and not poison. We swallowed it down with a gold tooth smile.

The English language is dry and deficient in the words of love, pride, hope, and spirit (that's why Abdel-Halem sang in Arabic). There are just too many words for hate, poverty, hunger, and fear in English. Those are the words that wrap themselves around our tongues and squeeze this story out of them. Wrap themselves around our necks and squeeze the life out of us. This story is about how words can weigh you down like a heavy feather.

 THROUGH my cheap Medicaid glasses, I could see the other kids sporting Menudo key chains and t-shirts. Everyone had to have a favorite member in elementary school, there were cliques named after Miguel and Xavier. The cartoon show came on every Saturday, and we'd hear their prepubescent voices straining with the dry English words. Our tv had awful reception. Still, we'd play with the antenna until we got them on one of the Spanish stations. That's where they'd really shine, with their Farrah Fawcett hair and Michael Jackson socks, them little boys were every little girl's wet dream.

MY PARENTS told me it was a sin to worship humans. We could only praise Allah. I'd try to explain that the heroes of the youth were just cool, not gods, but it wouldn't do no good. I was sure that the Devil was up to no good, 'cause my parents kept saying I was sinning every time I did something. I had a way to get him back though.

See, I had it all figured out. He lived in the sewers. I knew where he lived; God was upstairs, and the Devil was down. Whenever I got beat or yelled at (usually both), I'd just keep stomping on the floor until I knew I'd given the Devil a headache. Then he'd have to go to sleep, and I'd have some time alone. I wouldn't just stomp, no, I was too religious for that. I'd spit. I'd spit this story out of my mouth until it burned a hole through the floor and landed on Iblis's head, heavy like a rock. The floor would be so wet afterwards, I'd slip on it. It didn't matter though, 'cause I was doing God's work.

On the plane coming to America at age 5, I looked to find Heaven in the clouds. Started to hallucinate. I saw one of God's big eyes floating around. That's what I used to think God was, one big eyeball. God saw everything you did, especially the bad, and made a record of it so you'd get yours in the end. As I slept, behind closed doors, in the bathroom, watching the kissing scenes on tv, the eye was watching. I would wonder if God also saw the things, especially the bad, that men tried to do behind closed doors. Why didn't the eye cry out a heavy drop of rock to stop it? I know now that the eye looks away sometimes. I know now that I can't afford a blink.

 I PERFORM my ablutions in this wet that dares me to dry my hands of it. Knows full well I can't shake it off my skin. The pen in my hand becomes slippery and falls to the floor where my spit directed at the Devil still singes the thin carpet. I gotta pray, write this story, get some peace. That's what has replaced the eye in my mind. Peace. Too many spirits have been weighed down under tents and stone roof units. Rinsed out of the open sewers of the camps and the yellow water of the projects.

MASSACRED blood flowed from the Sabra and Shatilla camps to enter the Brooklyn water system. My horror at the newspaper reports could only guess at the number dead. I could hear the shrieking and wailing of the old women as they sifted through bodies in search of one who belonged to them. I was too young to hear so many names not mentioned 'cause the news wouldn't take the time to find them out. They were just dead. The only teacher to let me know it was alright to cry was Ms. West, my only Black teacher. She held me as I cried over these people I didn't know, and she cried with me. My other teachers asked me, What did I expect? My people were terrorists. They got what they deserved. My tears turned to stones to hurl at them.

The first time I heard the word *intifada*. How beautiful it sounded rolling off my tongue. Ain't no word in English equivalent to this one. *Intifada* means fever. The type of fever which releases a long sickness. The word was used to describe the popular Palestinian uprising of the mid-80s. Trembled inside as I watched young men with the *kafiyehs* round their faces throw rocks at the soldiers. I remember the pride I felt every time I'd see a lone girl in there with the guys. I'd love that girl and envy her for being there. As the news cameras were forced to broadcast the effects of the *intifada*, the Palestinian martyrs became known as professional victims. Professional political analysts would sit there on tv, in their ties and suits, and talk about how these kids in jeans and flags were just looking for attention. Talked as though their hands weren't wet with the blood of ugly un-televised deaths.

Them young kids inspired an entire generation to write poetry, to sing songs, and to write stories of resistance. Pictures of South Africa I saw looked like the pictures of Palestine, only darker. A moot point. South African youth would throw whatever was nearby at the soldiers who kept them down. I saw the rocks of crystallized revolution being thrown in Brooklyn too. I stood up in class one day and let my teacher know that I was a Palestinian, and that we did exist as a nation, as a people. My love over the ocean wasn't enough to stop the rubber bullets from killing or the bulldozers from demolishing homes, but I've kept my eye and heart on Palestine, since I saw that first stone thrown. I haven't turned away. I haven't blinked.

Breaking fly in high school.

THIS WET was on Coltrane's tongue as he laid out his sad story. I heard it slither into my ear from my headphones as I was writing poetry one night. Dew of night flowers leaped onto my page, and the words became part of the low trumpet moan and the high sax sigh. I tried to shake it off me with the sway of my hips, but my skin only absorbed the sweat, and it became a part of me. The part that has no rest, no sleep, no peace, until I'm dried out.

BRAIDING my hair after my shower, I plaited this story onto my head long ago. Locked into the hair of Toni Morrison and Alice Walker, the moistness of this story dropped onto their pages and into my lungs. The shock of white hair that the woman Rabab, the Palestinian activist, grew overnight after the Sabra and Shatilla massacres, wet itself with the tear drops of these words. The cool wet of the power of the erotic warmed my hands as I held Audre Lorde's voice in my hands, turning the pages as though poetry were my life's breath. The words I write were present on the cheeks of the Queen of Sheba and on the scissors of Delilah. The tale I tell lived in the afros, locks, braids, and curls of the world's beautiful and strong.

MY PRIDE writes of the first time I heard Hanan Ashrawi control an entire room, filled with obnoxious reporters; I wanted to sit down and write her a thank you letter. Speaking their language better than most of them, she handled them like a teacher with kindergarten kids. Answering with ease and power, she stood her ground despite the downpour of antagonistic questions. I told my father: "See, a woman can do anything a man can do and sometimes better. She's even Palestinian." He shot me down with one of his frequent, "you don't know anything" looks. "Do you know what she had to do to get there?" he asked. A woman was nothing without her bed. Her wet bed.

 THERE'S this wet that comes from nowhere and kisses my lips, bites my cheeks, and frizzes my hair. Soaked in words that have nothing to do with anything. About everything that I've ever loved or was. I told you that I don't drink. I lied. I imbibe this libation of words as though it were nourishment. I wrote that I don't smoke. Another lie. Rolling up these pages, I set fire to them once they touch my dry mouth and breathe in the mist as though it weren't poison. I'm addicted to this story and its juice. Need a daily fix. Need these drops in my blood, otherwise, I bleed too freely. Need this story to thicken my anemic blood and cleanse it of its daily pollutants.

BILLIE HOLIDAY poured the honey of this all over the microphone. She sang it in her own addicted voice. Had Malcolm X listening to his own story through her song. Part of this story dropped down these pages from the martyred blood that dropped from Malcolm's wounds. My tears fell as I finished his autobiography, how he wet my eyes with love, hope, and pride. El Hajj Malek el-Shabazz taught me more about Mecca through his words than any imam or any man. Malcolm X taught me more about God through his story than any holy book or holy war. I didn't expect him to die at the end. I knew it, but didn't expect it. I struggle to mold these drops into a bouquet worthy of perfuming his grave, worthy of his perfume. The tears of his little girls and his blood mingled to become the inspiration of a whole generation's stories, poems, and songs of resistance. The love of a whole generation waters the flowers that adorn his spirit.

I know that Hammad and Malcolm chill out together in Heaven. Feel it in the rain that layers the concrete. They tell me to perform my ablutions in this story. Direct my pen eastward. They say to open my mouth and swallow it all down, this rain. Hearing them call my name, I know my ancestors are with me.

THIS STORY was juiced out the *intifada* stones thrown over the sea. I drank down the desert's sweat until it burned a path down my throat. Drips down my shirt and wets my flesh with the hot, sandy liquid. I swallow the toxic elixir of this tale and spit it out.

 SOME people are lucky, they can afford the good stuff. Can afford Jack Daniel's and Black Velvet. Others get by on malt liquor. This story ended up in the bottom of empty forty-ounce bottles of Crazy Horse and Country Club. Rolled under my feet in bottles that were already drained by ten in the morning. You'll never find ads for ghetto poison in certain real estate areas. The stories on the billboards of Harlem and Flatbush tell of little boys who drink beer out of baby bottles. I wanted to write this story in high school, when this Puerto Rican kid in class showed me how his hand was shaped as though wrapped around an eternal forty. This kid, who could hardly read the words country club, much less belong to one, woke up and went to sleep drunk. He was proud though. At least he wasn't a junkie, at least he wasn't a crackhead like his cousin. Some people can afford good stuff for their weaknesses. Others have to make visits to the corner bodegas several times a day, until they fall asleep to dreams of Billy Dee Williams, crazy natives, and waltzes they'll never be invited to.

THE HEAT of these words shoveled a hole in the hard ground. Eleven years old and asking my cousins to show me the bathroom. I remember their laughter as they took me. I had never seen no toilet like this before. Getting off the plane from New York, I was tired, thought maybe I was imagining it. The bathroom was a small closet with a hole in the ground. There was no "please don't squeeze" tissue, no seat, no little man in a boat. My cousins pointed out the water handle dangling from the low ceiling and left me to my business. I didn't use the bathroom for three days. I was in pain. I finally told my father, and he yelled at me for being too American. Then he let me go over to my maternal aunt's house. They had a regular toilet. I decided to sleep over there for the rest of the trip.

 THE KIND of wet I'm talking about burns holes through paper, shirts, flesh, and souls. No rain gear can resist. Feeling tired and dry, I've cried while these drops hit me from every angle. Kind of wet don't allow you to wait it out in a doorway. I read and re-read my poetry, feeling a little bit of this story in every poem. I read and re-read my life, wondering why I seem to be the only one soaked to the bone. Wonder why every one else seems cool and dry.

Already bored with this wet that won't let up, I've wanted to give up. Walked out of school after writing for hours. Frustrated, why am I the only one soaked to the soul? Crossing the street to get the paper, it took some time for me to realize I was getting wet. Literally. It was raining. Not just any rain, my rain. These words. The annoying wet that don't stain the concrete, but bites your face. I got kissed on the back of my neck. Just finished crying ugly, dry tears, trying to get this out my system. Now laughing like a maniac in the middle of the street. The only one out without an umbrella.

This is the story about how, just as I was ready to stab my pen into a garbage can and rip these pages up, I drank. Remembered the sweet taste of it. Rode the wave back to control these words and write. About how God made the angels' tears cover my own. It all tasted good.

THE WATER boiling for tea had a story to tell, I just didn't know it. I know now that these drops brewed in the after dinner tea I'd make for my parents every night. The mint leaves I'd drop in would fragrance my tiny hands, as tea burned my flesh in Beirut. In Beirut, I had steaming tea dropped on me twice in the same month, accidents. Lucky, we were sharing our apartment with a young medical student who took care of my burns. People were dying all around us. We were in the middle of a war. It was too hard to get a four-year-old baby with second degree burns to the hospital in the middle of a war. I can remember the feel of my raw flesh brush up against the rough cotton of my father's borrowed pajama top (the only thing I could wear till I was healed). This story was in that water that ate into my young skin. My burned belly swallowed a mint leaf, and it grew to a bush inside me. I bear its fruit on these pages. Drink its nectar along with the bitter tea of Beirut.

I can remember Sabrine's birth. Born in Beirut. Remember clearly how the ugly midwife shooed us away. This lady's mustache was heavier than the air strikes above our heads. She cursed out all the kids of the building. Told them to go play, this was woman's work. Shut the door in my face. But I saw her place one of them large aluminum tubs underneath my squatting mother before the door ended my view. The tub that people washed dirty clothes in, that was what my sister got as a safety net for her birth. That and the sound of guns and bombs. This is the story of our welcome into the world of war.

THE WAR that devastated Beirut and welcomed Sabrine has visited me everywhere. I'm used to seeing the bloody sights of it, smelling its burning tires. This story is my refusal to accept it. In Brooklyn, you could get shot for wearing the wrong look, or the right sneakers. In Lebanon, neighbors were killing each other over who had the better god. Meanwhile, little kids couldn't get to hospitals, and babies were born in tubs. 'Cause war is too busy for anybody else. The holy wars and the drug wars are being won. By the Devil.

I once believed I could die for country, father, god. I now write that I would live for them. I'm sick of fighting. Exhausted by battles I did not choose. I gotta pick my battles 'cause there are too many out there to let them pick me. I'm sick of this wet. As though it were a blessing and not a nuisance. Nourishment rather than poison. The war goes on in my head, with the enemies being one and the same. I'm in war with God, daring my opponent to let me win, just this once. This story has me war weary and dry eyed. This war has me waving my empty pages as a plea for mercy.

My sisters - Sabrine, Suyan + me.
We used to sing "We are family".

LEAKED into my cheap snow boots as I walked, in knee-high snow, home from school. I know now that I was carrying it in the wet of my socks and in the cold of my toes. I would need to wear three pairs of socks and two pairs of gloves, and I'd still freeze my butt off. This story was in the cocoa and soup from packages my mother would make for us on those extra cold days. I drank it down without knowing it would stay inside of me, only to warm me into submission years later.

 THIS WET is the most valuable resource on the planet. Will nourish the crops of Palestinian farmers, whose water supply is sucked up by big brother. Water the parched deserts and thirsty throats. Drops of this pen will thicken anemic blood and clot the flow of deaths. I know that this ablution will cleanse me of my sins. It has to.

Torture. The words shame me into writing about real torture. Interrogations of Palestinian youth. How cigarettes and knives are used to drain confessions from scared, landless boys. Real torture, not this watered-down, struggling artist crap. Maybe I am too American, too used to bottled water.

SOMETIMES I think that I can fry plantains and falafel in the hot oil of this story. Get so heated and upset, I just want to burn something. The time I heard them white girls order falafel in their oh-so-cute voices. They wanted it extra crispy, as though it were some fried chicken or potato chips. I wanted to let them know that falafel is only made two ways; good and not good. Didn't say anything, just kept chewing my kebob sandwich. Almost choked when I heard them ask for "ghummus" on their sandwiches. Wanted to tell them it was pronounced *hummus*, and that they were putting too much on their food. I kept chewing. Didn't say a word. When they were walking out, I heard them talking about how much they loved Israeli food and wasn't that belly dance music oh-so-cute? I swallowed it down. Wanting to belly dance on their heads. This story was in the can of Pepsi I had to drink to force my food down my throat. These words in my throat, and all I wanted to say, pushed down into my belly.

THE VERRAZANO bridge crossed the mass of these words, as my family's American dream came true. Their own house on some land. I still didn't get my own room, but there was a lot of grass and trees. Actually, there were manicured lawns and detailed landscapes. Staten Island was, is, a totally new world. Ordered nature. A nasty, pretty, dry planet. If Brooklyn had soaked me in this story, this new suburb of a borough was now wringing it out of me. If I had ever entertained the notion of being slightly better 'cause I was slightly lighter, Staten Island let me know that any shades other than pale winter pink and temporary summer tan weren't cool. They let me know it with their oh-so-polite questions regarding what I was. What the hell was I?

What did you say? Pakistani? Which one of your parents is black? Hablo espanolo? I bet you can dance real good. Can you rap? Can you cook curry?

I'm Palestinian. I'd have to point it out on the map (the region, not the name).

Oh, you're Israeli! Did any of your family survive the holocaust?

Reply that my people were living through their own holocaust. Teachers would challenge me:

There's no such place as Palestine. Where is it on the map? Why do you people make so much trouble? Don't you know what the Jews have been through?

That's when the kids would realize what hell I am.

You're a terrorist. One of those animals that bombed the marines in Lebanon. Those gypsies who hijack planes and kidnap athletes. We know about you. Terrorists. Animals. Murderers.

Their words dropped on me like air strikes above Beirut.

 THE NEW kids I went to high school with were into some old other shit. I had never seen so much hair in my life. Girls would spend a good can of hair spray a day on their gigantic mall hair. Book bags were filled with exotic gels and spritzes, not books. The bathrooms were always crowded with girls putting on their faces in front of dingy mirrors. These kids had the money to spend on $70 jeans and $100 boots, regularly. Came to school in BMWs and Benzes.

Football and cheerleading were the kicks for the popular kids. The keg parties held every weekend spilled this story into the Atlantic and over to Brooklyn. Some things weren't so different. Most of the students were having sex, only here, the parents took them to get good birth control and sometimes abortions. So the neighbors wouldn't know. Kids took drugs just like they did in Brooklyn, but here crack wasn't the flavor like pure cocaine or steroids. Stashes were hidden in cars and used up during lunch time. Staten Island youth aren't into Colt 45 as much as vodka, the white kids anyway. Most of the kids of color are ghettoized. Living in their own refugee camps. Some get to mix real well with the white kids, almost as though they were that cool shade of white. Until the oil and water separates, and they realize that they're only called on for basketball games and international food fairs.

 SWAM the ocean to be written. I wrote this out in English class in high school, while my teacher kept her eye on me, 'cause she was sure I was gonna cheat. She was so busy copping me, wouldn't notice the other students scheming right under her nose. These drops dripped off the Shakespeare I had to re-read so new teachers would believe that I understood it.

SPRAYED stiff into the permed hair of white girls who would ask me if I was sure my hair was naturally curly. They'd look at me as though they felt bad for anyone who hadn't paid for her curls. I watched them same girls, and their boys, change over the years. The kids who once wore their hair Barbie straight, and their jeans skin tight, soon began to don base-ball caps and baggy jeans. House music was replaced by rap, and jeeps ran over Fire Birds. The thing was, I felt sorry for them. We all go through changes, but these kids totally changed. As if they had no center. How can you overhaul so drastically, unless you were never grounded to begin with? I felt sorry for them in their fake tans, fake hair, fake selves. I'd feel sorry for them, until they'd ask me if I could cook curry.

THIS WET tangled my hair into knots that the comb couldn't get through. I wrote this story while my mother was trying to braid my hair into a decent appearance. Most of the Puerto Rican girls had fine, baby doll hair. Asian girls had hair that just fell like water. White girls could pay enough money to make their hair look however they wanted. The black girls had hair that could hold braids for weeks without getting messed up. My hair was somewhere in the middle, just like me.

This story is about how the middle is too wide and too narrow a place for anyone to live in.

 I WRITE of how color does matter. Matters on the inside and out. On the outside, I dance between a sallow yellow when I'm sick, to a brilliant bronze when I'm cool. On the inside, I'm as black as a Miles Davis bruisey moan and as white hot as a cold surf.

 THIS IS the story about how you always get only what you can handle, even if you don't wanna admit your strength. Sometimes it's easier to believe that you're weak. Then you don't feel too bad when you quit. Other times you have no choice but to finish, even when your head is bending under the pressure of heavy wetness.

MY MOTHER drank this liquid in as it rolled down her face from swollen eyes. What did she expect from her man? What can a woman expect from a man who has the open option of marrying three other wives? This story is about the too many women who live in abusive marriages, 'cause it's a bigger shame to be divorced than to be beaten. These words write about how arranged marriages become deranged lives. Too many names make up this story. Too many girls who had to learn patience and obedience. Patience is the woman's key to heaven. That's what men teach little girl brides. Them same men figure that they'll slide right through the pearly gates, 'cause all them male prophets got their backs, are looking out for them. Right in, even though they fornicate, abuse, rape, and war. Just get by, riding on the backs of little girl brides.

It's not like any culture treats its women any better than another. I write of Yemeni women getting kicked in the neck by husbands not happy with dinner. Latinas getting beat by boyfriends who didn't like the look on some face. Black women getting dogged for their money by junkies and hard up gamblers. White women getting their faces smashed into windows after leaving an abortion clinic. It ain't like anybody can point a broken finger at anybodyelse. Women. This story is about women, and how patience ain't some damn virtue. It's a threatening chain of socially accepted submission that has got us down for the count. The drops keep counting off.

 CLEOPATRA bathed in this milky liquid centuries ago. Khadija swallowed this brew while charging horseback in the name of Allah. Remember that these women whispered in my ear that patience is cool as long as it ain't killing you. I swim against the torrent of words that come out wet with a story old as kohla-rimmed sight. I swim against tide of this tale. Come out having died eight times, and a little wet behind the ears.

 A DROP licks my ear. Wish upon a street lamp. Listen to the flow of the living in sewers. Stay up at night wondering who gets to fall in love. Dig being my own woman and all. Appreciate the time vibing with the universe me, the inner me and all that. Just wonder why I gotta do all this stuff on my own. Wanted to ask them Jehovah's Witnesses that come knocking on my door. Do onlya few people get to fall in love, the way only some get to heaven? Hope not. Maybe it's the kind of people who win the lottery or graduate college in four years. Damn, I hope not.

 STIRRED into the heavy Arabic coffee and Café Bustelo of my childhood. Don't like coffee too tough. When I was little, Arab women would tell me that young girls who drank coffee would grow heavy mustaches. Didn't need that. There were other warnings from these frustrated women who found themselves in loveless marriages. Like, a girl who curses has the Devil in her mouth. Too bad, 'cause I can cuss like a sailor. Like, a girl who wore tight jeans wanted boys to touch her, and a girl who lets boys touch her was no good. No good was the girl who looked grown men dead in the eyes and told them to stop feeling up on her, 'cause you wasn't supposed to look no man in the eyes. It was a come on.

Wet gossip filled my young ears. These women would talk about how so and so's husband was copping some female. The voices would be hushed and devious, as they slurped their coffee and smoked their hidden cigarettes. Good girls didn't smoke either. I used to feel my ears burn up with the name of the poor soul who found herself under them heavy tongues.

These women knew they were talking about themselves the whole time. It makes it easier to complain when you use another name. Bore babies like it was going out of style, while cooking daily feasts for adulterous husbands. They talked about each other and Allah. Money too, but mostly they talked about going home. About how life in this here *Amreeca* was lonely. Missed their parents and sisters. Their kids knew only that their mothers didn't speak English and believed in virginity. Didn't know that each woman had cried words out her eyes and mailed the wetness via air mail to her family and land overseas. They couldn't know that each woman drank that strong coffee in memory of neighbors who stopped by to chat or of aunts who brought holiday gifts. How could we know that our mothers were here before us? All we knew was to be good girls, or you'd find your sorry self underneath a sad tongue.

 THIS WET sprayed out a can of roach killer, across fake wood paneling. The thing about Brooklyn is you get used to the smell of bug spray and the cold of radiators. A human can get used to a lot of shit, otherwise why do we accept 75 percent of the things we do? Got used to the sight of the homeless asleep outside in the snow of their stories. Hate that accommodation of the soul. When I think of all the people hungry and cold in their alone, I try to cry to get the pain out. I can't anymore. Don't know what's sadder; the misery of the world or that we no longer cry over it.

I ASKED Ms. West to lend me a thin book on slavery in the third grade. Held the pages to me tight, my pillow soaked by my futile tears over little African babies. I cursed the gods who had allowed little black babies to be enslaved like work roaches. Wanted to go back and burn up all the men who had sold lives as though they were their own. This story dropped from my eyes, as though my tears could bring them babies back to life. Give them each a can of bug spray to fight the enemies of humanity with.

SEARCH through the Bible only to find that Moses parted this sea years ago. Jesus turned this story into wine and drank it down with that communion cracker of his. The Quran tells of how these words are forbidden unless they are told to a spouse. Search the holy books and holy wars to understand this eternal wetness. I come out with more questions than I had before I opened them books.

WISH I had this wet to ease my dry throat a bit as I got lectured by my dad. Why did I get a 90 rather than a 100 on my exam? Even at age eleven, I was to be perfect. He'd ask how many kids in the class did better than me. It didn't matter what I answered, I was gonna get it. Then he'd go on asking, maybe those kids' parents worked harder than he did? *No, dad.* Or maybe they loved their kids more than he did? *No, baba.* Or they beat their kids more? *I don't think so, daddy.* I was supposed to come up with a good excuse about why I wasn't the best, or I'd get a 100 percent ass kicking. Of course, he was still gonna get me, so I didn't think too hard. I'd just pray he'd use his belt rather than his open hand. Tasted this story travel down cheeks as I promised that I'd do better next time. Wiped away these words from my face as he told me to go wash up, then give him a kiss, and ask his forgiveness for being so stupid.

Years later I shoved this wetness down my throat, refusing to let baba see me cry. I prayed to God to keep my eyes dry until I reached home. As I drove the car, my father was yelling at me about how he was letting me go to college. He was doing me a favor. I had to be a grateful daughter and study what he wanted me to. I was to become a doctor. End of discussion.

At 20 - chilling in a restaurant.
Check out the Kool-Aid Smile.

I waited until he'd gone to sleep to cry. By that time it was three in the morning (he had a lot to add). Tried to squeeze the tears out of my eyes. Nothing. Where had they gone? The entire ride I had struggled with them, now, here I was willing them to drop. I didn't cry that night. I wrote. I've written ever since (and long before), and them tears have been shed, only not the way I'd expected them to.

I understand now my father really thought he was doing me good. Education means a lot to Palestinians. We've become some of the most educated people in the world through our diaspora. We've had to be. When you ain't got land, your degree may be your only solid ground. My father felt (feels) that being a doctor would give me security. How can I explain that I'm not safe from anything if I don't write?

 THE WHITE kids in Staten Island got me thinking about all their questions. What am I? I asked wise women. Some answered, you are the place you are born. I was born in a refugee camp in Jordan, but never belonged to those hills. Others said, you are what your family tradition wants you to be. I'm Palestinian, even though I have yet to set lips on that land. My heart drips with the blood of a nation called Palestine, even if I have yet to feel her between my toes. The wisest of these women answers: You are what your experiences make you . . .

an olive pit sucked real good and spit out of
   Palestine
ocean tide that licks Puerto Rican beaches to salsa
   beats
rise of cornbread in an old stove with collard greens
   on the stove
the lock in a girl's hair as she jumps double dutch on
   concrete
the little girl who whimpered "no"
ash of phosphorous bombs dropped in Beirut
warm spittle on Coltrane's reed
teenager who shared her nightmares with a stuffed
   bunny
spirit of dance slave who bathed in the Nile
bubbles of a newly opened Pepsi can
sister of the tabla
cousin of the conga
tightly wrapped grape leaves
frustration sprayed onto subway and store fronts
sweat jumping off the necks of kids playing handball
   against bodega walls

All of the above and more. I no longer excuse myself for
being all and more. No longer apologize to others who can't
understand that this wetness has bathed me now, as the
Nile did centuries ago.

THE STARS that scar the sky cried heat showers that came down my head like meteors. The words seared these pages as furiously as I wished upon stars as a kid. I wished for a lot of things, mostly world peace and an end to hunger. I also prayed for new jelly sandals, and them charm necklaces with fruit on them. Prayer was wasted on hoping that goofy kid in math class would like me, and getting some new jeans. Prayers are recited all over the planet for cars, drugs, ass, and yarnhead dolls. Prayers for food, peace, home, and justice are downed out in the wetness of greed.

Little kids wanted to grow up to be movie stars. Acting out famous movie scenes on Brooklyn stoops. Too bad all Latina girls had to play sluts. Asian boys had to be grocers. Black boys, thieves and pimps. Someone always had to play the Indian. Too bad the slut was always shot, the grocer always robbed, the thief always lynched, and the red land was always stolen.

A WOMAN writing a story about nothing but words and their wetness. Wonder what people will think. My friends will kick my ass if they get bored. But I'm just trying to be done with this wetness. A Palestinian woman speaking for herself, without some sympathetic anthropologist talking for her. A poor kid who grew up to tell the stories she lived. The want of my feet for Palestinian soil and Brooklyn concrete. The itch of fingers for a hand to hold. Burn of heart for a lover. The tear of my eye for some peace.

A Palestinian writing about the L.A. uprising and the slaying of Yusef Hawkins. About the burnin' and lootin' of L.A. and the *Intifada* stones hurled by burning tires. The murder of Yusef bought to mind the lynchings in the South and the assassinations in the East. Watched the riots on tv, as I had the *intifada*, as I had Yusef's funeral. As I had too many events and deaths. Television had become an extension of my pen, every newscast birthing another horror. Another frustrated poem.

A woman telling the only way she thinks how, hoping someone will understand her words. Praying someone else will wet her soul with these same words. Knowing that she has to shake these drops off her and just hope to hit the right people.

THIS STORY was spilled on to the sea from an oil tanker whose captain was too drunk to steer right. The words coated the fish and layered the coral.

 TO THE flow of a beat box, dripped from leaky faucets into rusted sinks. Spread like government cheese on Goya crackers, and swallowed down with malta. In school, we mixed them into the Vaseline we slathered on our faces before fights. The slickness on our young faces would make it hard for an opponent with a blade to do much damage. Schoolyard fights were decided on during lunch, and by three, your earrings and chains were being held by friends. The only jewelry worn were the name rings that clawed two or three fingers into a weapon. Hair was pulled back with the ghetto's barrette, a rubber band. I know now that all them fights can make you stronger, but I wish there was some other nourishment to give our kids. Too bad we have to remember Vaseline and blood as the cocktails of our youth.

PUMPED out of the bottles of curl sheen. Use the colorful words to polish nails. Spread the meaning of this madness across lips, shinier than any gloss. Don't need blush, even on sallow days. Line eyes with the lines of these page, ink as kohl. This beauty is of earth, ain't no plastic here.

Kneaded into the skin of beautiful tired women, this wet tried to reduce the visible signs of aging. Smile lines after years of forcing pleasant faces to a world that hated them. Told their value lay in their looks, were sold face creams and youth lotions, as though they were blessings. Selling their souls, these women bought up these prayers in a bottle with food stamps and welfare checks. Bleaching their hides to reach an impossible shade of porcelain, Arab, Latina, and African women compared each other's progress in the fight against their own natural faces.

The story about the acceptance of tired, sad beauty that radiates with the love of mothers and grandmothers. Tired and sad beauty that's more genuine than any poison in any bottle. It don't sell itself, or buy others. These drops travel down the cheeks of women who have forgotten that God held each of their noses in divine hands and shaped them into perfection. This drop falls on to the tips of

Semitic noses and quivers, then joins the ink on the page. I write this love song in the name of our mothers' beauty, to let them remind themselves that we were beautiful before there was Revlon.

SCRUB all the labels and names that cling to me. Too bad we gotta call ourselves by man-made borders, languages, or hair types. But if I didn't name myself Palestinian, who would? Too bad we can't go by the names of our spirits rather than the width of our noses, and whatever is resting between our legs. For all the nonsense about domesticity I put up with as a kid, my father really did raise me as a boy. I was encouraged to think, to ask, to figure out. Just couldn't act on anything. My father raised a strong human being, but when he realized I wasn't gonna grow a penis, he changed his mind. Thank God it was too late.

Scrape away all the shit that men decide they wanna call me, 'cause they can't pronounce my name or my spirit. I shield my body with the thread of this wet. Protect myself from the cutting gaze of horny drunk men on street corners with these pages of wet steel. Wash away the greedy stares of business men on their way to buy the world, with the soap of these words. By the end of the day, I'm layered with grime of unwanted looks and unsolicited remarks. You would swear that women walk around naked, with big "take me" signs on their chests, the way men push up on them. I've gritted my teeth on too many subway rides, while some fool pressed himself against me. Lowered my gaze from too many pairs of bold fish eyes, sizing me up for dinner.

 THERE'S this story that keeps falling on my head. The thing is, it comes down wet. Not like some big-ass storm, but a pleasing kind of kissing rain. The kind that makes sidewalks slippery and night flowers open up to the moon. The type of liquid that flows out of liquor bottles into hungry stomachs. Wets the pages of books and stains your hands with the bloody ink. Wetness that soaks souls and dries tears. Flowing through open sewers, this story washes my body in the love of a far away nation and the lust of a caressing city. Frizzing my hair, bites the back of my neck, just to let me know it's there. Open my mouth and stick out my tongue, to taste drops of this story, me.

Swallow it, no, gulp it down. As it travels up to my eyes, cry drops of this story, only to lick it off dry lips in need of a kiss. My tongue is now accustomed to the hot, sweet taste. My throat welcomes it to my belly. I write of love, pain, and words, colors, and music, rain. I slip into this wet and stand in the middle of the street, to taste, to cry, to spit, to sweat drops of this story, me.

DROPS OF THIS STORY
is set in HIROSHIGE, a typeface designed in 1986
by Cynthia Hollandsworth of AlphaOmega Typography.
HIROSHIGE was originally commissioned for a book of
woodblock prints by Japanese artist
Ando Hiroshige (1797–1858).
Most of the ornaments used in this book
are modifications of arabic geometric designs
from *Desk Gallery* (Dover Publications).